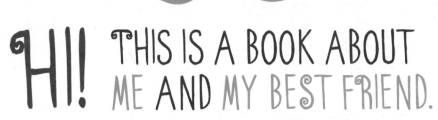

HI! THIS IS A BOOK ABOUT ME AND MY BEST FRIEND.

PLACE YOUR PHOTO HERE

MY NAME IS...Hailey...........
MY BEST FRIEND'S NAME IS...Bella.........
DATE...5-28-2013..........

~ALL ABOUT US~

My best friend and I met at ....

That was .... years ago!

The first time I knew we would be best friends is when ....

....

ME

I am .....7..... years old.

My birthday is ....

My best friend's nickname for

me is ....

....

My best friend would describe

me as ....

....

My best friend is special because ....

....

....

....

....

MY BEST FRIEND

My best friend is .....7..... years old.

My best friend's birthday is ....

My nickname for my best friend is ....

....

I would describe my best friend as ....

....

My best friend thinks I'm special because ....

....

....

....

The best way to describe
my best friend is:

Friendly

Shy

Smart

Sporty

(Boy Crazy)

Totally fashionable

Inquisitive

· · · · · · · · · · · · · · · · · · ·

When my best friend and I
are together we are:

Silly

Adventurous

Out of control

Calm and quiet

Always cracking
each other up

· · · · · · · · · · · · · · · · · · ·

JUST THE TWO OF US

I can always count on my best friend to ·

· ·

My best friend can always count on me to ·

· ·

The one thing that can always make us giggle is · · · · · · · · · · · · · · · · · ·

· ·

When we're apart, what I miss most about my best friend is · · · · · · · · ·

· ·

SUPER SLEEPOVERS

MY BEST FRIEND AND I LOVE TO HAVE SLEEPOVERS!

Our favorite munchies are:

Pizza

Popcorn

Cookies

Chips

Anything chocolate

. . . .

**During sleepovers,
our favorite things to do are:**

Watch movies

Play video games

Dance and sing

Talk all night

. . . .

The first one to fall asleep is usually . . . .

The first one to wake up is usually . . . .

In the morning, we love to . . . .

OUR FAVORITES

My favorite COLOR is Pink

My favorite BOOK is oned

My favorite SONG is ld

My favorite MOVIE is ld

My favorite FOOD is pasta

My favorite SUBJECT is math

My best friend's favorite COLOR is

My best friend's favorite BOOK is

My best friend's favorite SONG is

My best friend's favorite MOVIE is

My best friend's favorite FOOD is

My best friend's favorite SUBJECT is

PLACE A PHOTO HERE!

BEST FRIENDS FOREVER

PLACE A PHOTO HERE!

PLACE A PHOTO HERE!

HOLLYWOOD

LIGHTS, CAMERA, ACTION!

If there was a movie about me and my best friend, it would be called . . . .

. . . .

. . . . would play the role of my best friend and

. . . . would play the role of me.

Our theme song would be . . . .

If there was a television show about my best friend and me, it would be called

. . . .

My hidden talent is . . . .   My best friend's hidden

. . . .   talent is

. . . .

. . . .

. . . .

GIRL TALK!

My best friend and I can talk about anything!
I can always count on my best friend to:

Make me laugh — no matter
how down I feel

Not judge me

Be totally honest

Give me a pep talk

Just listen and
give me a hug

Just listen
and give
me a hug

Most of the time my best
friend and I talk about:

School

Other Friends

Sports

Movies

Television shows

Books

Our families

scool

HANGING OUT!

When we're together my best friend and I love to ....
....

Other friends that we like to hang out with are ....
....
....

My best friend would describe my room as ....

I think my best friend's room is ....

My best friend and I are totally creative. The coolest thing she ever made for me is ....
....

The coolest thing I ever made for my best friend is ....
....

PASTE A PHOTO HERE!

FUN STUFF!

My best friend and I love to:

Go bike riding

Go shopping

Go ice skating

Play sports

Watch movies
at the theater

Watch our friends
play sports

Hang out with our
friends

hang out
with our
friends

My best friend's style is. . . . .
. . . .

My best friend would say my style is . . . . .
. . . .

My best friend and I had the greatest time
when we went to . . . .
. . . .
. . . .
. . . .
. . . .

LET'S PARTY!

PLACE A PHOTO HERE!

PLACE A PHOTO HERE!

PLACE A PHOTO HERE!

PLACE A PHOTO HERE!

PLACE A PHOTO HERE!

PLACE A PHOTO HERE!

THE WRITE STUFF!

There are some poems, quotations, and song lyrics that sound as if they are describing my best friend and me. Such as...

....

....

....

....

....

....

....

....

....

....

....

....

....

....

....

....

....

TEN WORDS THAT DESCRIBE MY BEST FRIEND ARE:

1. ....
2. ....
3. ....
4. ....
5. ....
6. ....
7. ....
8. ....
9. ....
10. ....

TEN WORDS MY BEST FRIEND WOULD USE
TO DESCRIBE ME ARE: (ask your best friend to fill in this part)

1. ....
2. ....
3. ....
4. ....
5. ....
6. ....
7. ....
8. ....
9. ....
10. ....

SCHOOL DAYS

My school's name ...Hamilton

My best friend's school's name
...Hamilton...........

My grade ......1.........

My best friend's grade ..1...

How I get to school:

Walk

Bus

Car

Limo

Bike

Skateboard

...Car......

How my best friend gets to school:

Walk

Bus

Car

Limo

Bike

Skateboard

...Bus......

My favorite places at school:

Cafeteria

Gym

Playground

Playing fields

Library

Classroom

The principal's office

Art room

Music room

Science lab

.......classroom

My best friend's favorite places at school:

Cafeteria

Gym

Playground

Playing fields

Library

Classroom

The principal's office

Art room

Music room

Science lab

. . . .

My favorite subject is . . . .

My best friend's favorite subject is . . . .

My least favorite subject is . . . .

My best friend's least favorite subject is . . . .

I have a crush on . . . . Timmy . . . .

My best friend has a crush on Jack b . . . .

OUR DREAM

If my best friend and I could go on a dream vacation together, we would
go to ....
....
....

No matter what, we would pack these three items:

1. ....
2. ....
3. ....

We would like to travel with (friends and family members) ....
....
....
....

VACATION

On our dream vacation, we would definitely need:

Sunblock

Bathing suits

Winter coats

Walking shoes

Fancy outfits

Hiking boots

Sunglasses

. . . .

On our trip, we would . . . .

. . . .

. . . .

. . . .

. . . .

. . . .

. . . .

. . . .

HOPES, DREAMS,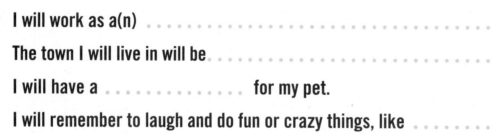
AND OTHER HAPPY THOUGHTS!

WHEN I GROW UP

I will work as a(n) . . . .

The town I will live in will be . . . .

I will have a . . . . for my pet.

I will remember to laugh and do fun or crazy things, like . . . .

. . . .

. . . .

WHEN MY BEST FRIEND GROWS UP (have your best friend fill in this part)

I will work as a(n) . . . .

The town I will live in will be . . . .

I will have a . . . . for my pet.

I will remember to laugh and do fun or crazy things, like . . . .

. . . .

. . . .

BEST FRIENDS

PLACE A PHOTO HERE!

FOREVER!

MY BFF

ILLUSTRATED BY: Bella

ME

ILLUSTRATED BY Hailey

THE END!

NOW YOU KNOW ALL ABOUT MY BEST FRIEND AND ME!

DATE . . . .